EGMONT
We bring stories to life

First published in Great Britain in 2018
by Egmont UK Limited,
The Yellow Building, 1 Nicholas Road, London W11 4AN

Content written and adapted by Catherine Shoolbred
Designed by Jeanette Ryall

ISBN 978 1 4052 9118 7
68610/002
Printed in EU

Parental guidance is advised for all craft and colouring activities.
Always ask an adult to help when using glue, paint and scissors.
Wear protective clothing and cover surfaces to avoid damage or staining.

Stay safe online. Egmont is not responsible for content
hosted by third parties.

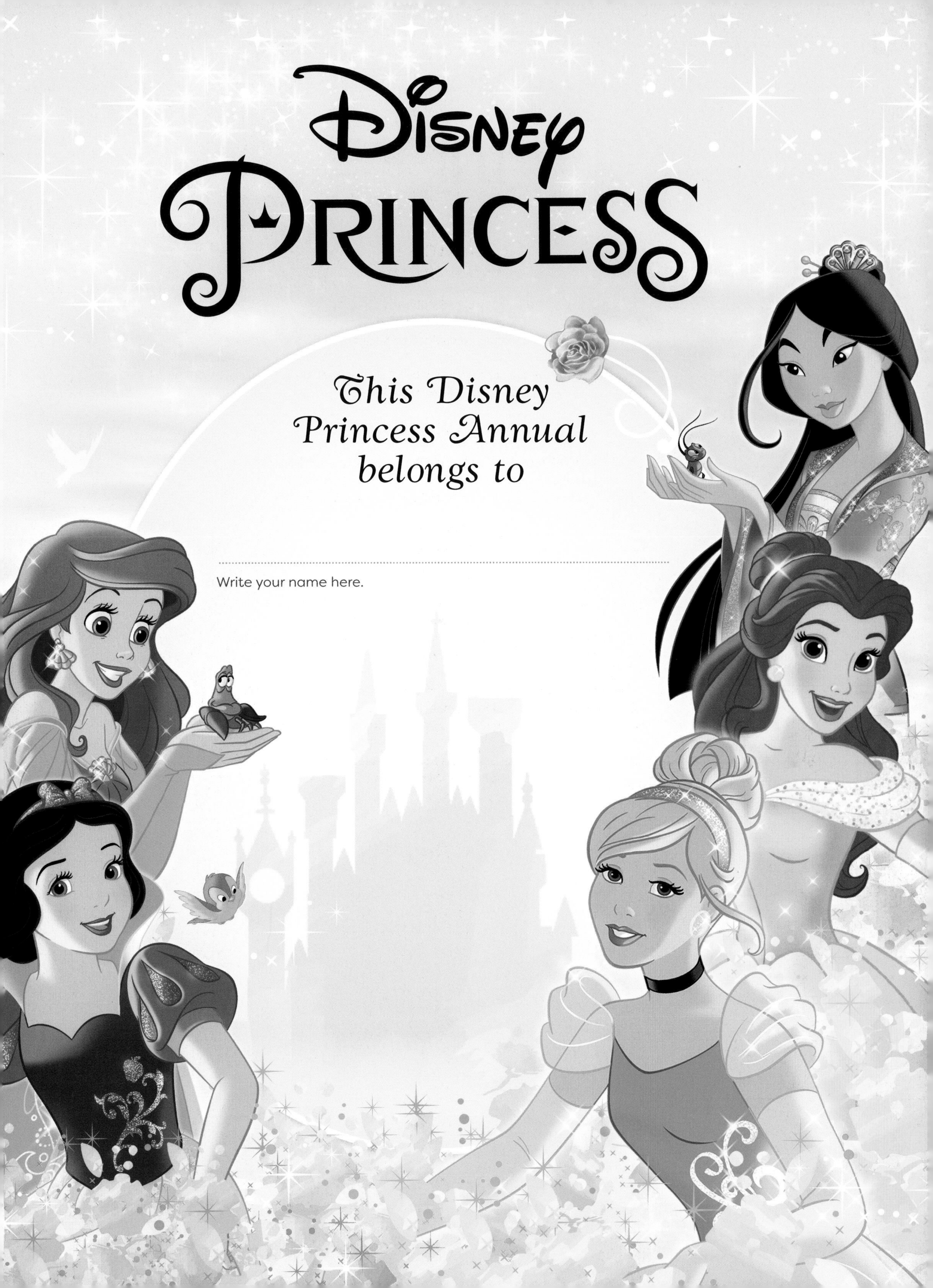
Disney
Princess
This Disney Princess Annual belongs to
Write your name here.

Disney Princess

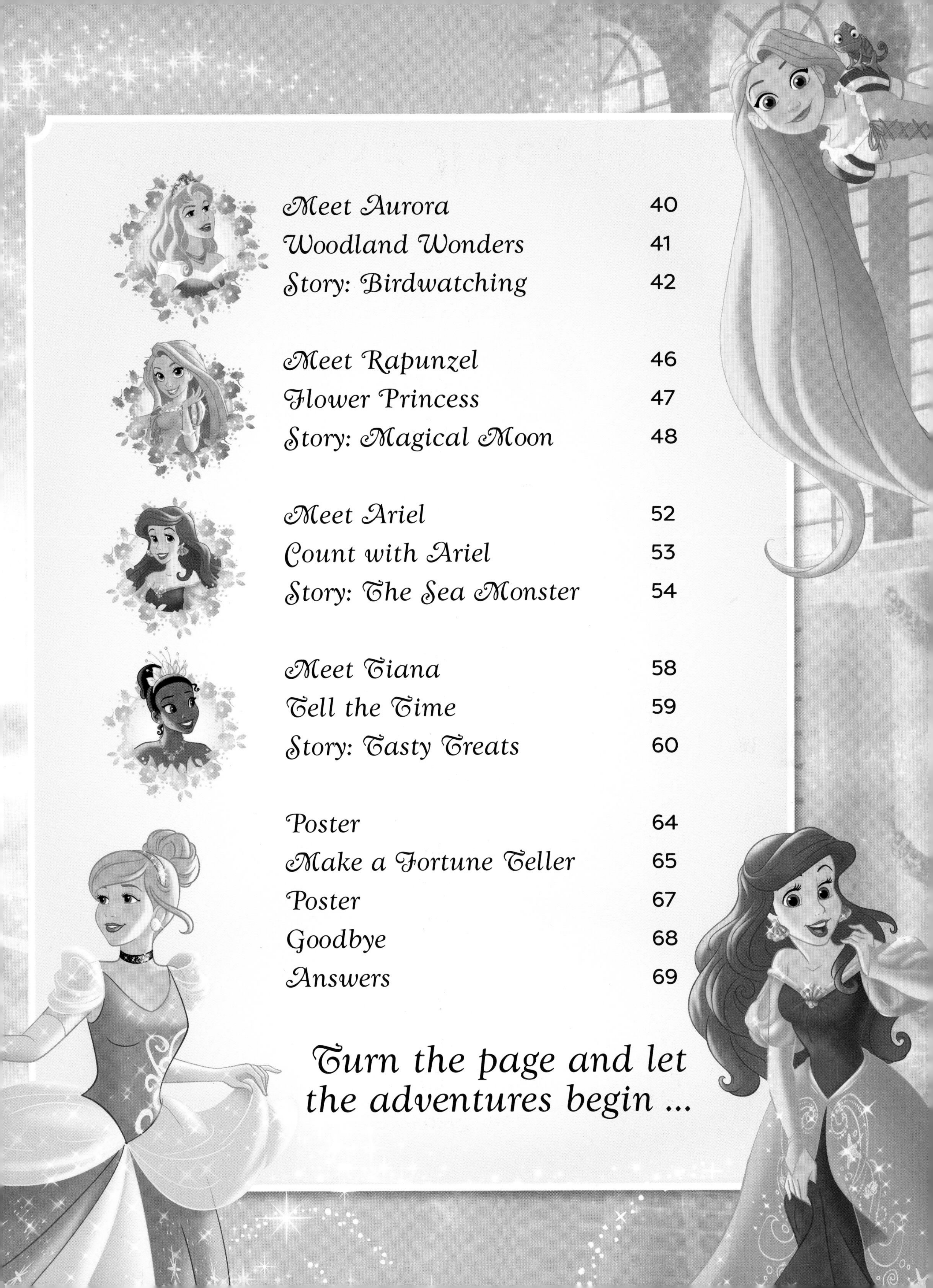

Turn the page and let the adventures begin ...

Meet Belle

All About Belle:

- She loves reading and learning.
- She wants a life of adventure.
- She fights for what's right.
- She looks beyond appearances and finds the beauty within.
- She isn't afraid to be different.

Belle's story

When her father is taken prisoner by the Beast, Belle takes his place and her new life begins. The Beast's castle is under a spell. Can Belle learn to love him and help him beat the curse?

Belle's Adventure

When Belle left her village, she set off on a great adventure!

1

Belle loves playing with Chip, the enchanted teacup. Can you spot the odd one out?

a b c

2

The enchanted rose is losing its petals. Put the roses in order, showing the one with the most petals first.

a 

b 

c 

a	b	c
	1	

3

Belle loves reading. Tick the shadow that matches the pile of books she's going to read next.

a 

b 

c 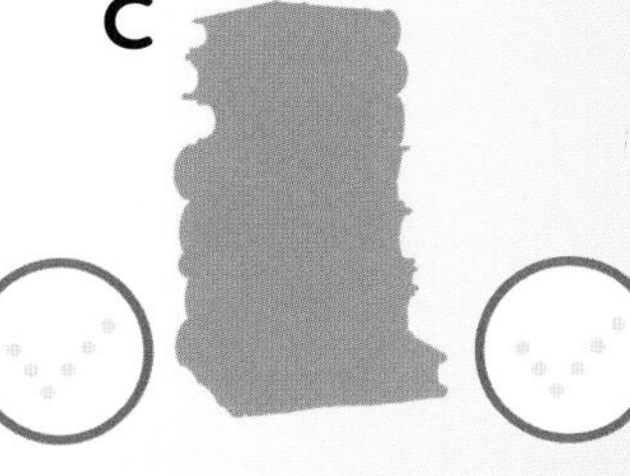

Answers on page 69

Belle's Books

1 Belle loved the castle library where the bookshelves rose all the way to the ceiling. One day the Beast saw her struggling to reach a book on a high shelf. "Let me help," he offered.

1 Trace the letters and read what Belle is trying to reach.

a book

2 But the Beast was too heavy for the wooden ladder! It broke apart and he fell. Belle rushed to him. "Are you OK?" she asked. "Yes, but this ladder is useless," he grumbled.

3 Belle decided to learn how to make a new ladder. "I think this book will teach me how," she told Chip.

4 Belle read everything about all the different woodwork tools and how to use them. Then she set to work building the new ladder.

5 When she had finished she proudly showed her ladder to her friends. “Amazing!” cried Lumière. “Do you know how to fix a chimney that smokes too much?”

6 “And a bell that doesn’t work,” added Cogsworth. “And a leaky kitchen tap,” said Mrs. Potts. “With the right book, I’m sure we can fix anything,” said Belle, setting to work.

2

Spot these characters in the picture above.

7 First, Belle found a home repair book. "I think the bell just needs to be oiled," she told Cogsworth. Sure enough, after a few drops it was as good as new.

8 Next, Belle found a book about chimneys. "According to this, the smokestack needs to be swept clean," she told Lumière. Belle grabbed a brush and soon the chimney was working perfectly.

9 Then Belle found a book about plumbing. To stop the tap dripping she needed to tighten the pipe with a wrench. The Beast helped her and together they fixed the leak.

3

Tick the tool Belle needs to use to fix the leaking tap.

a ◯ b ◯ c ◯ d ◯ e ◯

10 After all her hard work, Belle was feeling tired so everyone sat down for tea. "To Belle!" Lumière toasted. "And books," added Belle. "I couldn't have done it without them ... or you!"

The End

4 Match the books into pairs.

a b

c d

e f

5 Draw what you think Belle will read next in the space below.

Answers on page 69.

Book Maze

Belle loves to find fantastic books and stories in the Beast's library.

Answers on page 69.

Perfect Tiara

Take this quiz to find your perfect tiara.

1

Tick your five favourite pictures and match the colour you choose most often to the princess below.

Mostly blue
Like Cinderella you are loyal and helpful. Colour in the pumpkin.

Mostly purple
Like Aurora you are kind and caring. Colour in the flower.

Mostly green
Like Ariel you are fun and adventurous. Colour in the gem.

Meet Mulan

All About Mulan:

- She's fearless and ready for action.
- She loves and protects her family.
- She disguises herself as a man to take her father's place in the Emperor's army.
- She has help from Cri-Kee, a cricket, and Mushu, a little Chinese dragon.

Mulan's story

To save her father from going to war, Mulan disguises herself as a man to take his place in the Emperor's army. With a cricket and a dragon helping her, she fights alongside Li Shang to protect her family and village.

Dinner Party

Mulan is throwing a small party with lots of yummy treats for her two friends.

1

Find these four details in the picture.

2

Do you know the names of Mulan's two friends?
Trace the letters to finish their names.

Cri-Kee Mushu

3

Colour in Cri-Kee.

Answers on page 69.

To the Rescue

One day, Mulan was practising a type of handwriting called 'calligraphy' when her father's horse appeared at the window.

The horse whinnied for Mulan's attention. "What's wrong, Khan?" asked Mulan. Then she saw that her Grandmother's hat and big basket were still attached to Khan's saddle, but Grandmother Fa was nowhere to be seen!

Realising that Grandmother must be in trouble, Mulan leapt onto Khan's saddle and clung on, as Khan galloped to a nearby orchard.

Grandmother Fa was stuck up a very tall tree. "My ladder fell to the ground and broke," she said. "Please get help from the village before I fall." The village was very far away, but luckily Mulan had a better idea.

Mulan took Grandmother's basket from Khan's saddle and attached it to her sash. She threw one end of the sash over a high-up branch and attached the other end to Khan's saddle. As Mulan walked the horse slowly away from the tree, the basket rose towards the branches until it hung beside Grandmother.

"Step into your chariot, Grandmother," Mulan said. Grandmother Fa stepped into the basket. Then Khan moved slowly forwards, and the basket was gently lowered to the ground.

"You saved me, you brave girl," said Grandmother Fa, giving Mulan a hug.

When they arrived home, Mulan's father asked how her calligraphy practise had gone. But before Mulan could explain, her Grandmother spoke up.

"I helped Mulan today," her Grandmother said, winking at Mulan.

"What character did you practise?" Father asked.

"The character of courage," said Mulan, smiling at her Grandmother. "I had a great teacher!"

The End

Meet Cinderella

All About Cinderella:

- Cinderella is kind and gracious.
- Her stepmother and stepsisters treat her like a servant.
- Her animal friends make her happy.
- The Fairy Godmother's magic helps her attend the ball at the palace.

Cinderella's story

After her father died Cinderella became a servant for her stepmother and stepsisters. But when the palace announces a royal ball, a little magic helps Cinderella meet the Prince and change her life!

Helpful Friends

Cinderella has many animal friends, and they all want to help her out.

1. Find the six pairs of matching birds.

2. One of the birds has an invitation for the ball. Can you find it?

3. Can you spot the bird carrying a beautiful ring for Cinderella?

Answers on page 69.

Girls' Day Out

1 It was Girls' Day at the palace and Cinderella was hosting. She'd invited some girls from a nearby village to spend the day with her. "We've got lots of exciting activities to do," she told them.

2 First they flew kites, but Sarah, who had her arm in a sling, couldn't keep her kite in the air. Cinderella noticed and hurried away to find a solution.

1 Spot these colourful kites in the picture above.

3 A few minutes later she came back with a huge dragon kite. It had lots of strings so the girls could each hold one and fly it together. “I’m so pleased I can join in,” cried Sarah, happily.
Thank you, Cinderella!
4 “The next activity is a treasure hunt on horseback,” Cinderella told the excited girls. But Emma didn’t want to join in. “I’m scared of riding horses,” she said quietly.
This is the est treasure hunt ever!
5 Cinderella thought for a moment then had an idea. “You can ride with me in the royal coach,” she said. “Then you can still join in the fun.” “Thank you!” cried Emma.
2
Colour the coach.

6 Later, when the girls were having tea, Cinderella spotted Lucy standing on her own. She looked shy and Cinderella wanted to help her.

3 Match the cups to the saucers.

7 Cinderella noticed Lucy's pretty kitten necklace and introduced her to Alice. "She loves animals too," said Cinderella. Soon they were chatting away like old friends.

8 After a while, Alice stood up and thanked Cinderella for inviting them into her home and making sure everyone could join in the fun. "Hooray for Cinderella!" they all cheered.

Answers on page 69.

Get Active Game

2
Spin around two times.
3
Stand up on your tip toes three times.
4
Jump forward like a frog four times.

Meet Snow White

All About Snow White:

- She is kind and thoughtful.
- She loves taking care of others like the Seven Dwarfs.
- Her wicked stepmother treats her like a servant.
- Snow White loves animals as much as they love her.

Snow White's story

The Evil Queen, her stepmother, wants to kill Snow White, so Snow White runs away. She stays with the Seven Dwarfs in the forest, but when she's poisoned by a cursed apple, true love's kiss from The Prince saves her life.

Picture Puzzle

Today the Dwarfs are dancing in the meadow with Snow White.

Put the pictures in the right order by writing the numbers in the boxes below. We've done the first one for you!

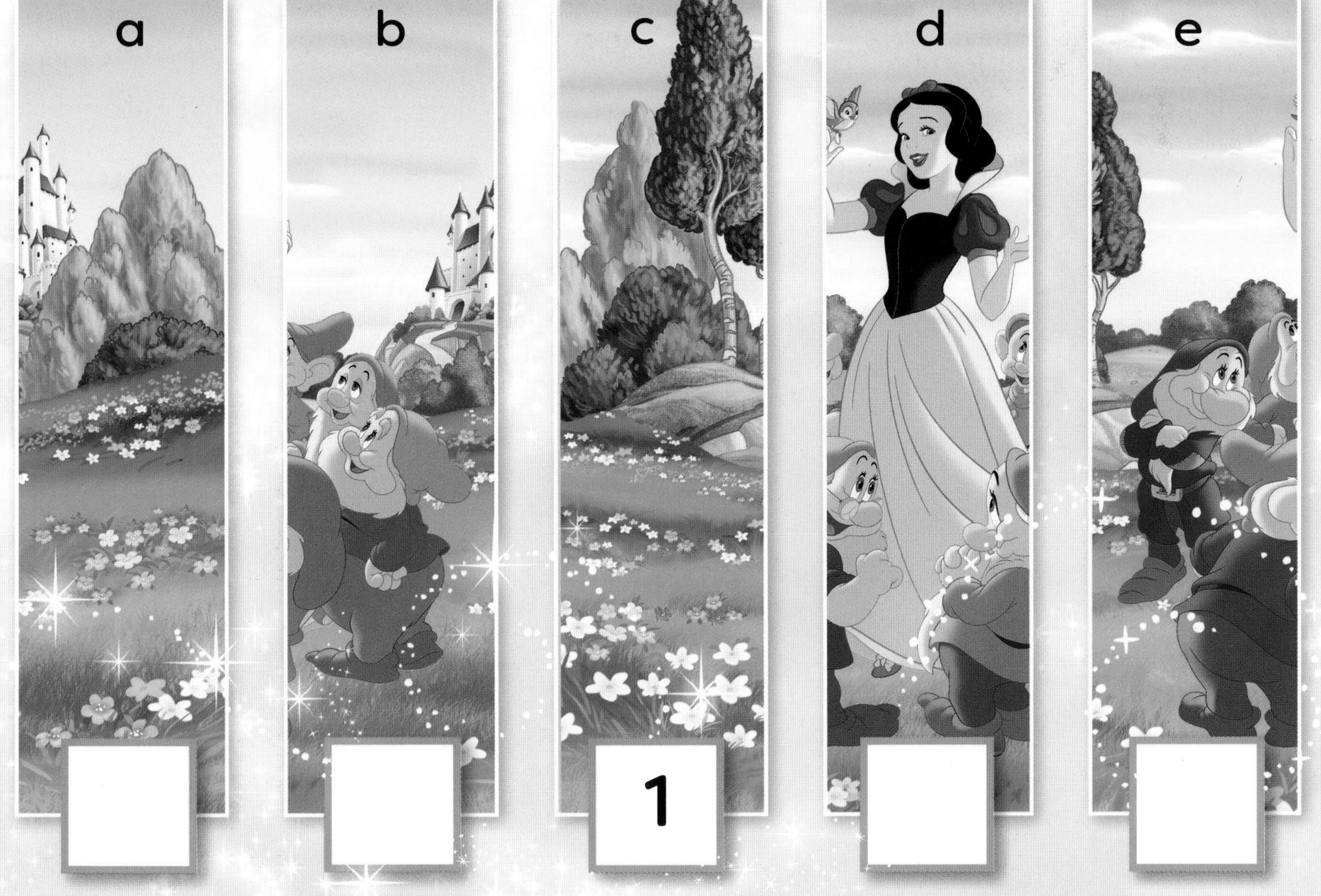

Answers on page 69.

Pumpkin Soup

1 When Snow White was a young child, she tasted pumpkin soup for the first time ... and she has loved it ever since. The soup always makes her feel warm and cosy inside.

2 One day, Snow White decided to make pumpkin soup for the Seven Dwarfs. So she asked Happy, Sneezy and Bashful if they could help her fetch a heavy pumpkin.

1

Do they want to help Snow White? Circle your answer.

Yes **No**

3 "We would help you but ... uh, well uh ..." stuttered Bashful. "We have to make sure the stream keeps running under the bridge," explained Happy. "That's right," added Sneezy.

Answers on page 69.

8 Then Snow White asked Sleepy and Doc to help her carve the pumpkin. But they said they just didn't have time.

9 Luckily, once again, Dopey offered to help. While Dopey carved the pumpkin, Snow White added herbs and spices to the soup.

10 The wonderful smell of the pumpkin soup drifted through the cottage and out of the windows. Soon all the Dwarfs had gathered around the dinner table.

11 Snow White and Dopey started eating their soup. "How about a bowl for us?" said Grumpy. "But none of you would help me make the soup," said Snow White. The six Dwarfs looked down at their feet.

3

Point to the Dwarf who helped Snow White.

12 Seeing how the six Dwarfs were regretting their bad behaviour, Snow White agreed to serve them some soup after all.
13 After the delicious dinner, Doc had a great idea. He told Snow White and Dopey to go and rest in front of the fireplace ...
14 ... while the others did the dishes and served them tea. Snow White smiled to herself. She knew the Dwarfs would always remember this day when she asked for their help!
The End
4
Spot these details in the picture.

Meet Jasmine

All About Jasmine:

- She wants an adventurous life.
- She loves to sneak out of the palace to spend her days in the marketplace.
- She falls for Aladdin's courage and sense of adventure.
- Rajah, her tiger, will do anything to help her.

Jasmine's story

Jasmine wants to marry for love and travel the world, but this goes against her father's wishes. When she meets Aladdin and goes on a magic carpet ride, her life will never be the same again.

It's Raining Sweets

Point to Jasmine and Aladdin in the picture.
How many children are there?

1

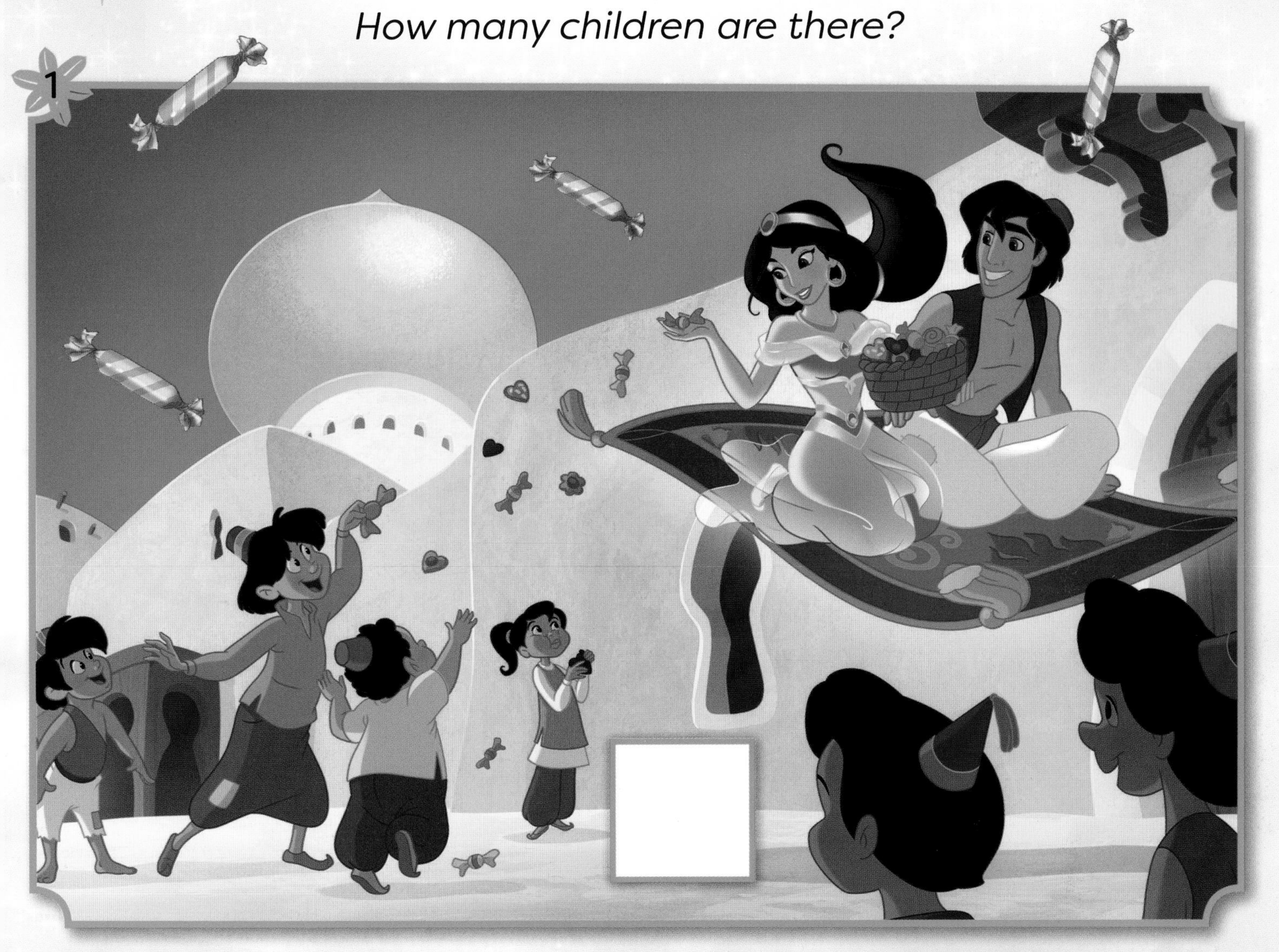

2

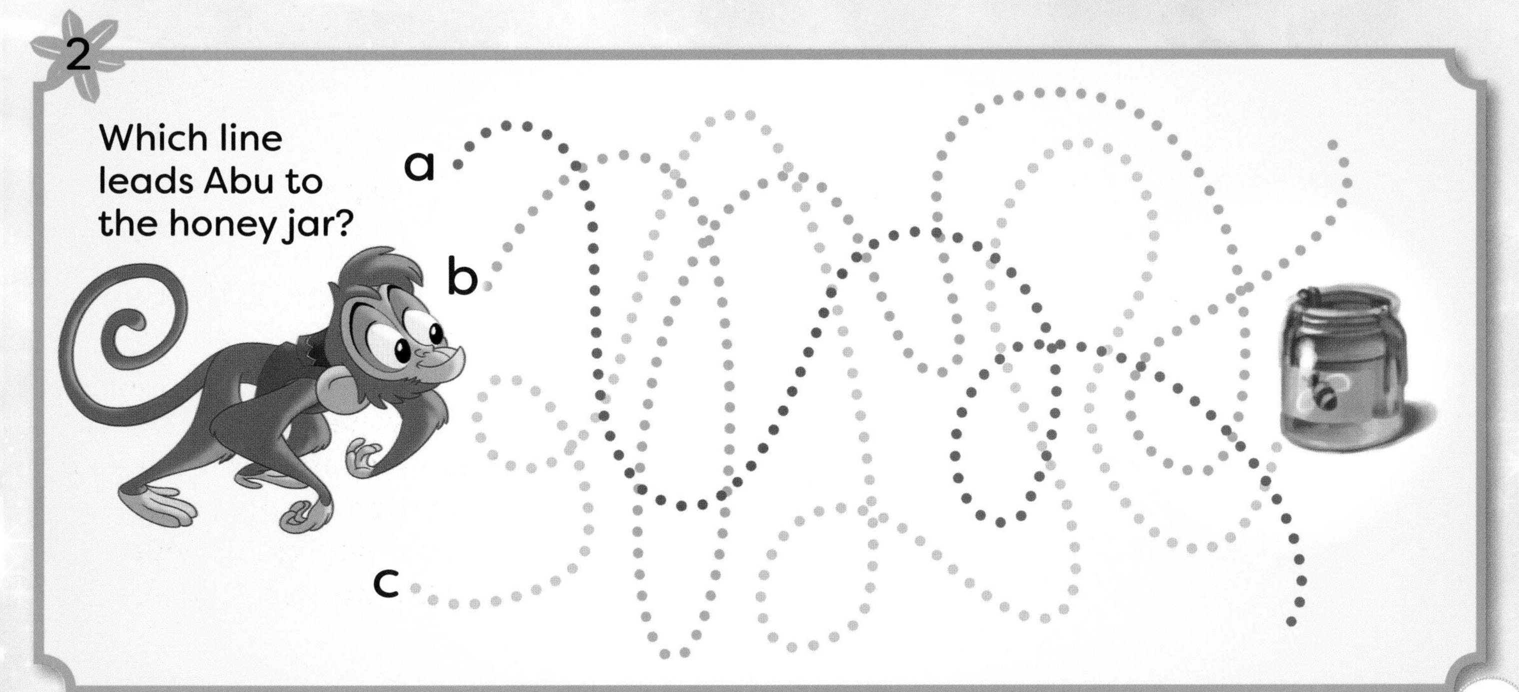

Answers on page 69.

The Disguise

The annual Desert Race was coming up, and the fastest horse and rider would be awarded the Golden Palm trophy. Jasmine's father, the Sultan, was upset because Prince Fayiz from a neighbouring kingdom had won it for the last three years.

"It's Agrabah's turn to win!" he cried.

Suddenly, Jasmine had an idea. "I could ride my horse, Midnight, in the race," she said. "He's the fastest in Agrabah." But the race was dangerous and the Sultan didn't want Jasmine to get hurt.

"How about I ride Midnight?" suggested Aladdin.

Jasmine took Aladdin to the stables but when Aladdin climbed on Midnight, the horse kicked and flung him off. He didn't want anyone but Jasmine to ride him!

On the day of the race Prince Fayiz looked confident, but as the race began a black horse with a mysterious veiled rider took the lead. As soon as they were out of view the rider threw off the veil – it was Jasmine!

"I don't like going against father's wishes," she whispered to Midnight, "but I have to show them we're the fastest."

As the race went on Jasmine stayed in the lead, but suddenly Prince Fayiz began to catch up.

The two horses were neck-and-neck but as they approached the finish line Jasmine shouted: "You can do it!" and Midnight crossed the line first. Jasmine had won! The Sultan ran over.

"I'm sorry ..." Jasmine began, but the Sultan was so excited he didn't mind that Jasmine had raced. "Agrabah is victorious at last!" he cried. "And it's all thanks to you and Midnight."

The Seasons

*A year is divided into four seasons.
The princesses love them all!*

1

All the animals have come to see Aurora. Colour them in.

Trace the word for each season.

spring

2

Count how many coloured butterflies there are in the garden. Then trace and colour this butterfly.

summer

3

Help Belle draw a line between each pair of leaves carrying the same amount of things.

4

Cinderella has been busy making snowmen. Circle the five differences between them.

Meet Aurora

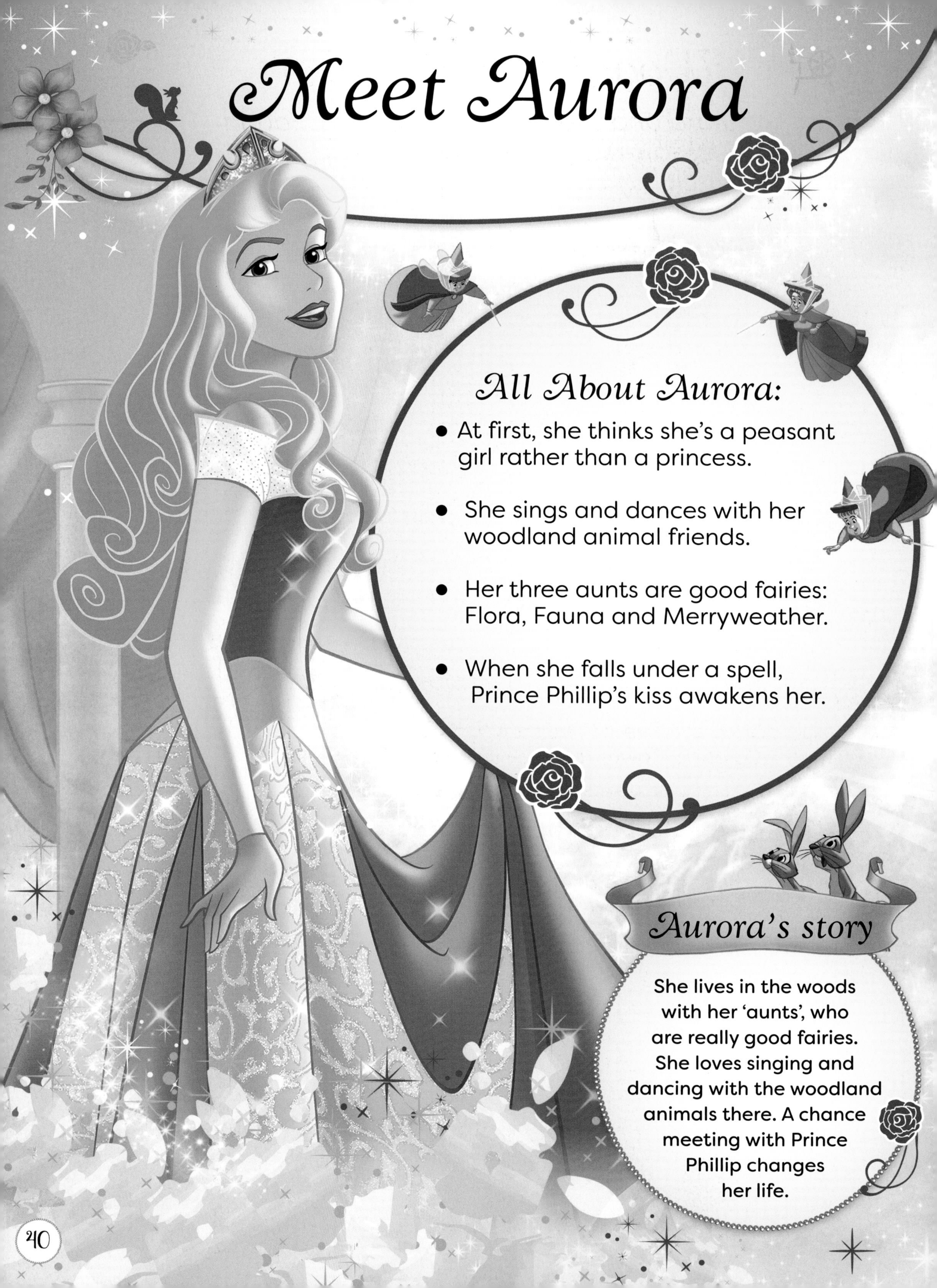

All About Aurora:

- At first, she thinks she's a peasant girl rather than a princess.
- She sings and dances with her woodland animal friends.
- Her three aunts are good fairies: Flora, Fauna and Merryweather.
- When she falls under a spell, Prince Phillip's kiss awakens her.

Aurora's story

She lives in the woods with her 'aunts', who are really good fairies. She loves singing and dancing with the woodland animals there. A chance meeting with Prince Phillip changes her life.

Woodland Wonders

Aurora and the three fairies, Flora, Fauna and Merryweather, are on a delightful birdwatching trip in the forest.

a

1 Spot the five differences in picture 'b'. Colour a flower for each difference you find.

b

Answers on page 69.

Birdwatching

1 One day, Aurora was in the forest with the three fairies. She had brought a beautiful book about birds and was reading about all the birds she could see around her.

2 "Look, there's a woodpecker!" said Aurora. "The book says that he uses his long beak to peck holes in trees to look for food."

1 Count how many holes the woodpecker has made.

4 or 6

3 The three fairies decided it would be fun to see who could find the most birds from the book.
Birds
4 "Let's see if you can spot this one," said Flora. "The book says it is very rare and difficult to find!"
5 "A little fairy magic will make this easier!" said Fauna, making the first bird she saw look exactly like the bird picture in the book.
2
Trace and colour the star coming from Fauna's wand.

6 Fauna continued to use magic to make the birds look just like the ones shown in the book!
7 "Stop!" cried Aurora. "Using magic to change their nature is not respectful to them!"
3
Add some colours and help the bird return to normal!
8 "It's much more fun to look around and see what you can really find," said Aurora. "Then we can use the book to learn all about the birds that live in our forest!"
Birds

9 Very soon the three fairies were having a wonderful time with Aurora's book and all the pretty birds in the forest.

The End

4

Find these bird eggs in the picture above.

5

Circle the animal who isn't in the picture.

a

b

c

Meet Rapunzel

All About Rapunzel:

- She has magical long hair.
- She is artistic and loves painting.
- She longs for a life beyond her tower.
- Pascal, the cheeky chameleon, is her best friend.
- Her parents send lanterns into the sky every year on her birthday.

Rapunzel's story

Mother Gothel takes Rapunzel so her magical hair can keep her young. She hides her in a tower in the woods. Rapuznel experiences the world outside the tower when she meets Flynn.

Flower Princess

Rapunzel thinks it's sweet of the three girls to braid and decorate her hair.

Answers on page 69.

Magical Moon

Oh, no! It's too cloudy!
4 But when Rapunzel opened her curtains the sky was full of grey clouds. "If the clouds don't clear by tonight I won't be able to see the moon and make my wish," she sighed.
5 All day Rapunzel kept checking but the grey clouds didn't go away. Pascal tried to cheer his friend up by making silly faces, doing a funny dance and popping up in unusual places.
Oh ... Hello, Pascal!
2
Circle your favourite funny face.
6 Despite Pascal's efforts Rapunzel still felt sad about the moon. "It's nearly evening," she said, as the cloudy sky began to darken. "I guess I won't see the full moon this month."

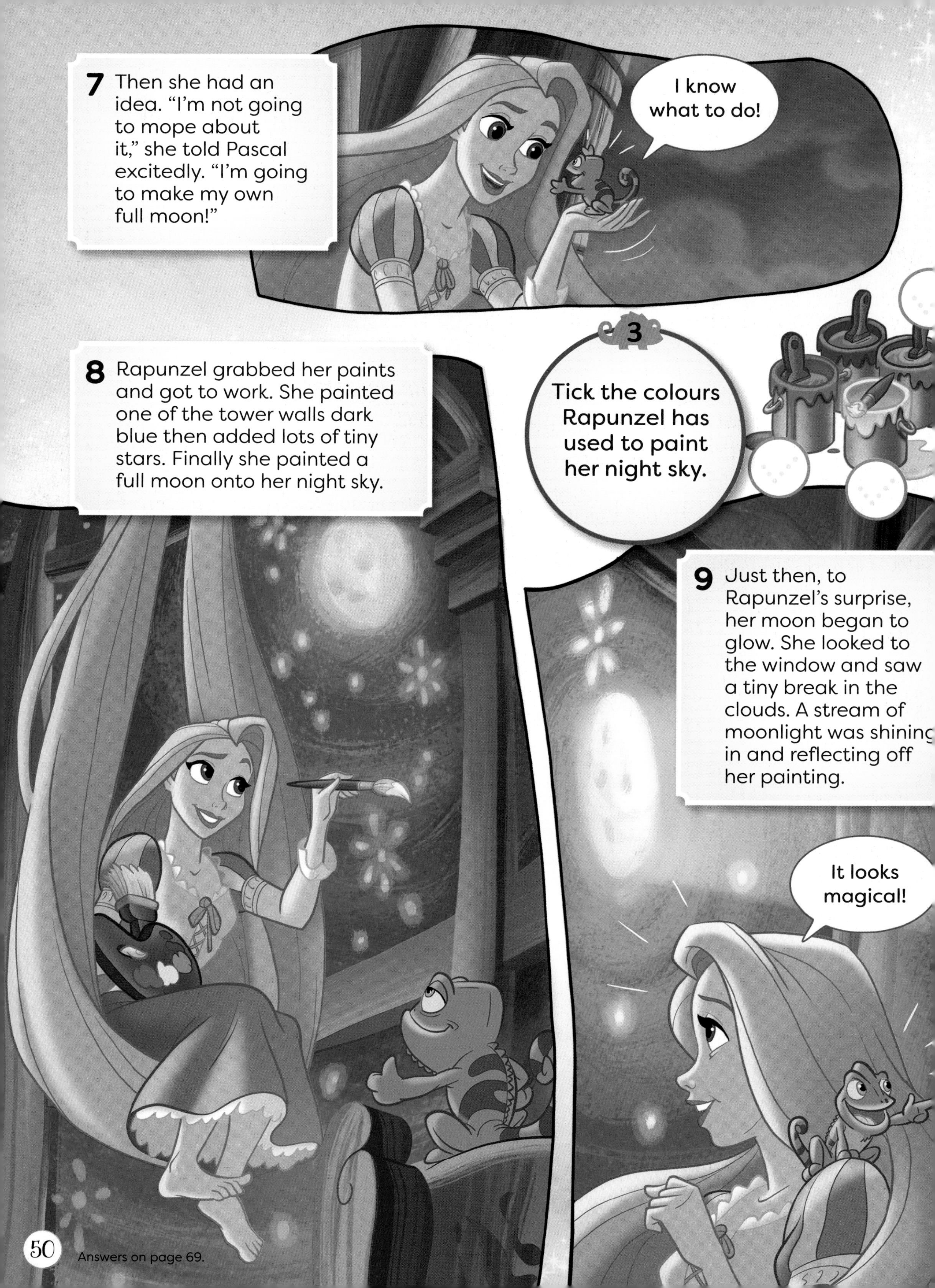

Answers on page 69.

0 Rapunzel closed her eyes and made her wish. When she opened them the clouds had covered the moon again and the moonlight had disappeared.
I'm glad I got to make my wish!
11 "The magical moon shone just long enough for me to make my wish," she told Pascal happily. "And hopefully this time it will come true!"
The End
4
Spot these items in the picture above.
5
Draw what you would wish for in the space.

Meet Ariel

All About Ariel:

- She is a headstrong mermaid princess, daughter of King Triton.
- She lives in a beautiful underwater kingdom with her six older sisters.
- Her best friend is Flounder, the friendly fish.
- She is fascinated by the human world.

Ariel's story

Ariel is the youngest daughter of King Triton. She wants to live in the human world, but her father wants her to keep away from humans. There are consequences when she goes against his wishes.

Count with Ariel

Ariel treasures every single human thing she finds in the sea.

Answers on page 69.

The Sea Monster

I'll help you.

1 Ariel had entered an art competition and was thinking of an idea for her picture. But everything she came up with was boring. "It needs to be original," she told Flounder.

1

Match Ariel's engraving pens into pairs.

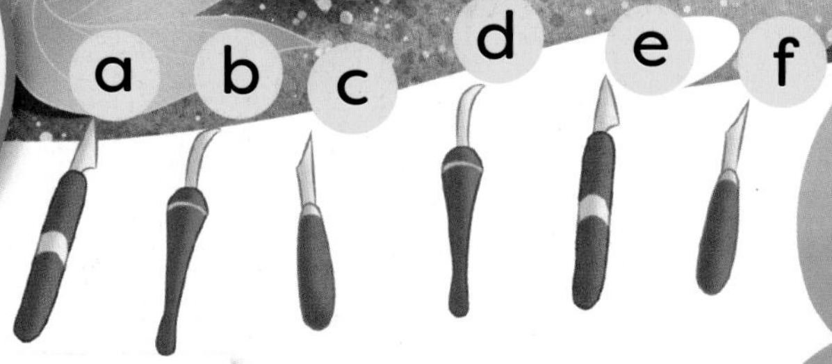

a b c d e f

2 Then Flounder remembered the sea monster that lived in a deep, dark cave. "If I catch a glimpse of him I could make a picture that no one's seen before!" cried Ariel excitedly.

Well done, Flounder!

3 The friends swam to the cave. It was very dark and scary. "Are you sure about this?" gulped Flounder. "Don't be such a guppy!" laughed Ariel, swimming inside.

It's a bit frightening!

2 **Circle the bag that matches Ariel's.**

Answers on page 69.

7 "You're not a scary sea monster after all!" exclaimed Ariel, as a giant squid came into full view. "No," said the squid, "but everyone thinks I am, so nobody visits me."
Come back soon!
8 "We'll visit soon but we've got to go now," Ariel said. "Thanks for returning my bag." As they waved goodbye, Ariel told Flounder the squid had given her an idea for her picture.
Wow!
9 On the day of the art competition, Ariel handed in her entry. It was a picture of a sea monster looking in a mirror at a reflection of a kind, giant squid. Everybody loved it.
Amazing!
I've never seen anything like it!

10 Ariel was given first prize. “I must share this with someone special,” she said. Ariel brought the squid to meet her friends and explained that he wasn’t the monster they thought he was.

11 “I thank you for helping others see me for what I really am,” the squid said happily. “And thank you,” Ariel added, “for inspiring me to make a truly original picture.”

3 Draw your own sea creature on the rock.

Meet Tiana

All About Tiana:

- She loves cooking for friends.
- She wants her own restaurant.
- She loves jazz music and dancing.
- She is best friends with Charlotte.
- When she agrees to kiss a frog, her life changes unexpectedly.

Tiana's story

Tiana is a hard-working girl who dreams of opening her own restaurant in New Orleans. One day she gets caught up in a crazy spell that transforms her and a prince into frogs!

Tell the Time

One evening, Tiana meets a very special frog. Draw the hands on the clock faces to show when she meets him, agrees to kiss him and has a big surprise!

At 6 o'clock Tiana's amazed to meet a talking frog.

At 7 o'clock she agrees to kiss him to break the spell.

At 8 o'clock she's horrified to see she's now a frog too!

Answers on page 69.

Tasty Treats

1 Ever since she was a little girl Tiana had loved to cook. She spent hours in the kitchen with her father cooking pots of gumbo and dreaming of the restaurant she'd own one day.

2 Now that she was older, Tiana got a job as a waitress. She saved every spare penny she earned but she still didn't have enough to buy a restaurant. "I need a second job," Tiana thought.

3 So Tiana asked Mrs. Johnson at the dress shop. "You sew well," Mrs. Johnson told her, "but I'm afraid I'm not hiring anyone until Mardi Gras." "I'll check back then," sighed Tiana.

4 Tiana's next stop was the DIY store. "Have you got any jobs?" she asked, as she grabbed a hammer to fix a loose sign. "I'm sorry, I've just hired my nephew," replied the owner.

2

Circle the items that belong in the DIY store.

a b c d e f

5 Then she asked at Cora's beauty parlour. "Show me what you can do," said Cora. But Tiana's hairstyle looked more like a wedding cake! "I guess it's not for me," she sighed.

6 Tiana's spirits were low so she went to Duke's Café for a rest. Buford the chef gave her a doughnut to cheer her up. "I guarantee it will put a smile on your face," he said.

Answers on page 69.

7 Back at home Tiana decided to bake a batch of beignets for Buford to say thank you for being so kind.

8 She delivered the tray of beignets to Buford straightaway. Their scrumptious scent wafted all around the café. "Can I try one?" asked a customer. "Me too!" said another. "And me!"

9 Word soon spread about Tiana's tasty treats and a long queue formed outside Duke's Café. But there weren't enough beignets for everyone. "Can you bake some more?" Buford asked.

3 Spot these hungry customers in the queue.

10 In no time at all, Tiana whipped up a big batch of beignets for everyone to enjoy, and Buford offered her a job as a beignet cook. She was one step closer to her dream.

The End

4

Count and write how many coins Tiana has earned. Trace the correct number.

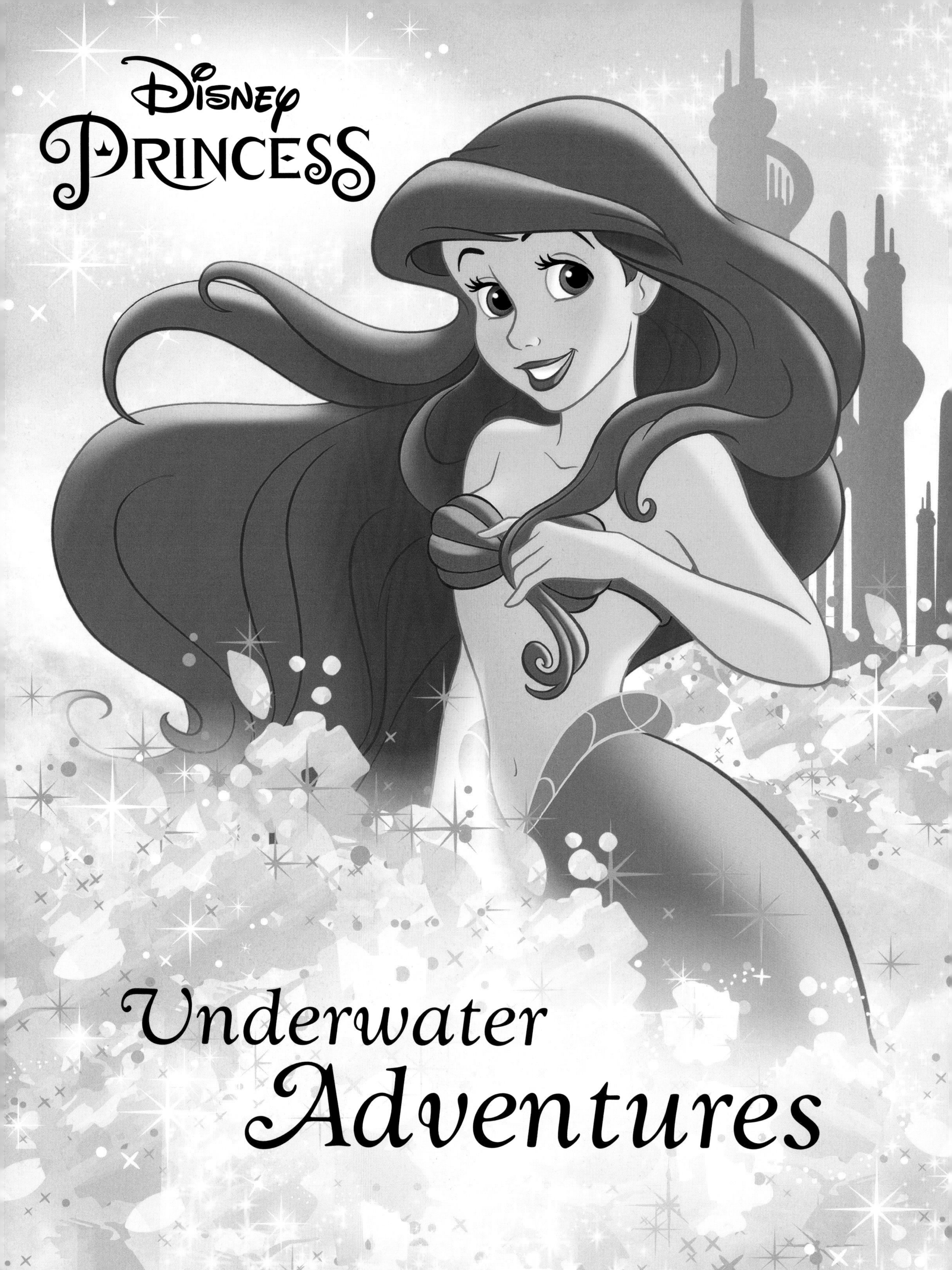
Disney
PRINCESS
Underwater
Adventures

Make a Fortune Teller

Have fun with your friends telling their fortunes.

Ask an adult to help you.

1. Cut out the fortune teller. Start with the pictures of Ariel, Cinderella and Jasmine face-up.

2. Fold and unfold along the four long, centre lines to make creases.

Key
– – Cut
—— Fold

3. Fold the four corners into the middle.

4. Turn over and fold the four points into the middle again, so the numbers are facing you.

5. Fold in half, and in half again, so the accessories are on the outside. Tuck your fingers into the outside flaps and open them up to start playing!

How to Play

Choose an accessory, count the letters in its name, then open and close the fortune teller the same number of times. e.g. tiara = 5 times. Choose another accessory and do the same again. e.g. handbag = 7 times. Choose a number and lift the flap to find the princess hidden behind it!

Fold along the solid lines.

Disney Princess

Follow your Dreams

Disney
Princess
Add your
photograph
or picture
here.
Thanks for
joining us!
We'll see you again
in next year's
Disney Princess
annual!

Answers

Page 9 *Belle's Adventure*

1) b
2) b, c, a.
3) c

Page 10-13 *Belle's Book*

1) a book.
2)

3) b, the wrench.
4) a-d, c-f, b-e.

Page 14 *Book Maze*

1) d

Page 17 *Dinner Party*

1)

2) Cri-Kee and Mushu.

Page 21 *Helpful Friends*

Page 22-25 *Girl's Day Out*

2)

3) a-f, b-d, c-e.
4) Gus is behind the teapot and Jaq is in the sugar pot.
5) skittles

Page 29 *Picture Puzzle*

1) a-5, b-4, c-1, d-3, e-2.

Page 30-33 *Pumpkin Soup*

1) no
3)

4)

Page 35 *It's Raining Sweets*

1) 6 children
2) c

Page 38 *The Seasons*

2) 6 butterflies
3) a-e, b-c, d-f.
4)

Page 41 *Woodland Wonders*

Page 42 *Birdwatching*

1) 4 holes (he's making a fifth one!)
4)

5) The squirrel isn't in the picture.

Page 47 *Flower Princess*

2) b

Page 48-51 *Magical Moon*

1) a-f, b-d, c-e.
3) blue and silver paint.
4)

Page 53 *Count with Ariel*

2) b

Page 54-57 *The Sea Monster*

1) a-e, b-d, c-f.
2) 3

Page 60-63 *Tasty Treats*

2) a, b, d and f.
3)

4) 8

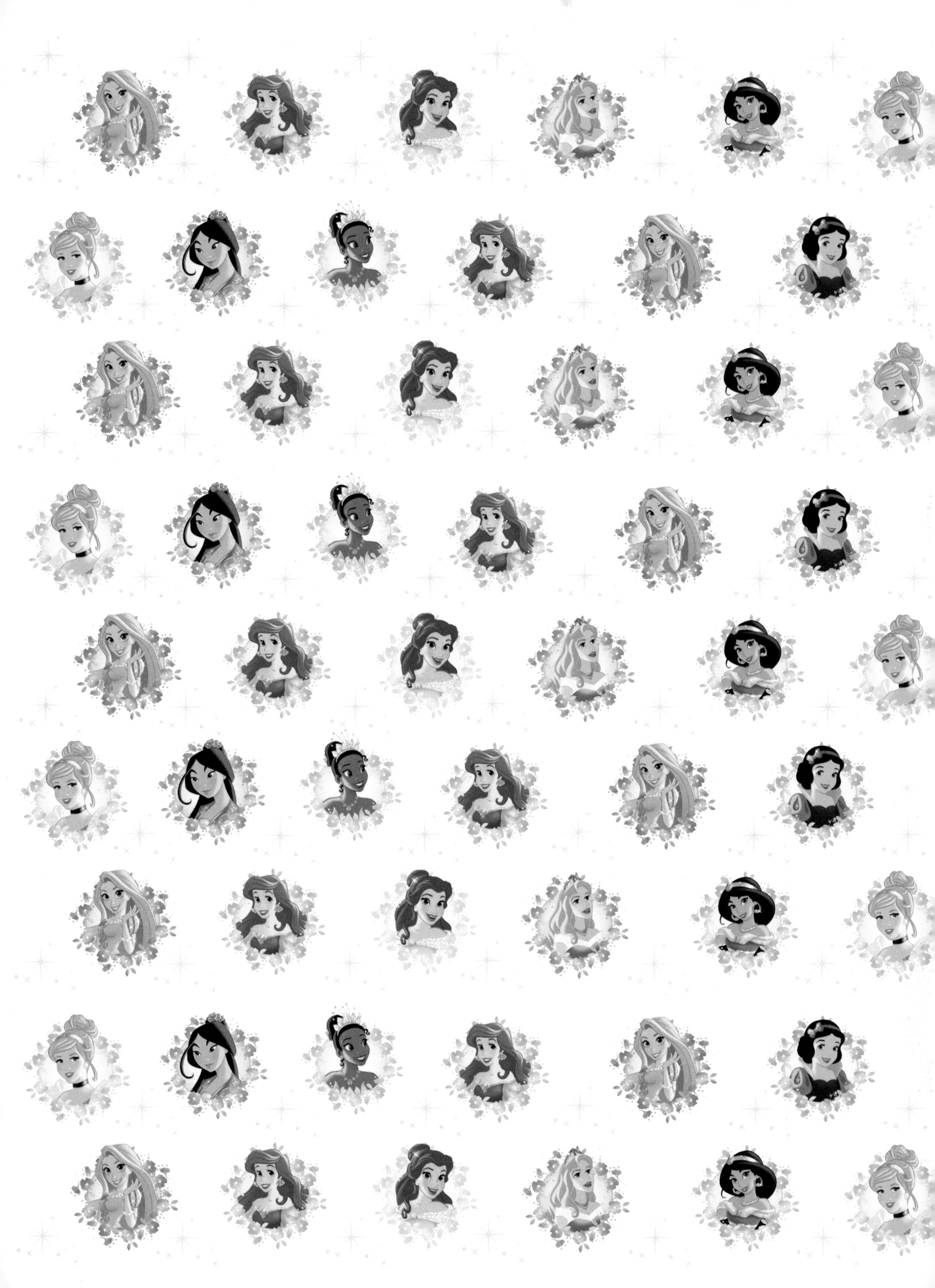